find your way

IN SPACE

Paul Boston

YOUR MISSION

The Zeebles need your help! Their rocket has crash-landed in Crater Canyon and they can't get home. Find your way to the crash site by choosing which exits or entrances to follow on each page.

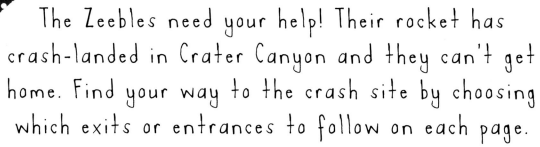

1
Choose your transport

Jet Pack

UFO

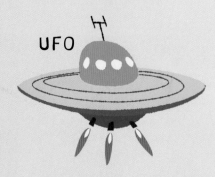

Space Camel

2
Trace a route

There are lots to choose from and you can go **BACKWARDS** and **FORWARDS** along the same tube.

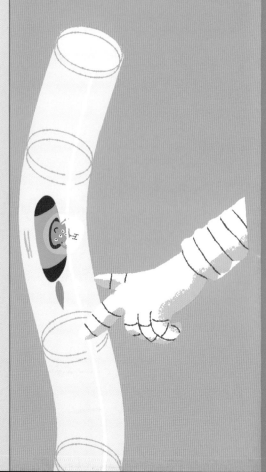

3
Collect on every page

Choose **ONE** of the missions below to help the Zeebles. You will find one of each object in every scene.

COLLECT 12 ZOBOGLOB BATTERIES to power up the engine.

COLLECT 12 CANS OF GLOOPY GLUE to mend the panels.

Collect **12 SPACE SPANNERS** to fix the rocket's wings.

4

Use the book LIKE A REAL MAP

Turn the pages and use co-ordinates in this book just like you would with a real map. You can find out more about co-ordinates on pages 4 and 5.

5

SOLVE maths puzzles

Along the way you will come across Zeebles who are lost or need your help. You will have to use your super maths skills to continue. You might be asked to count up to ten or to find a shape.

Welcome to outer space

Look at the map of space. Can you see where the Zeeble's rocket has crashed? That's where you need to get to. Let's use co-ordinates to help us describe where the rocket is on the map.

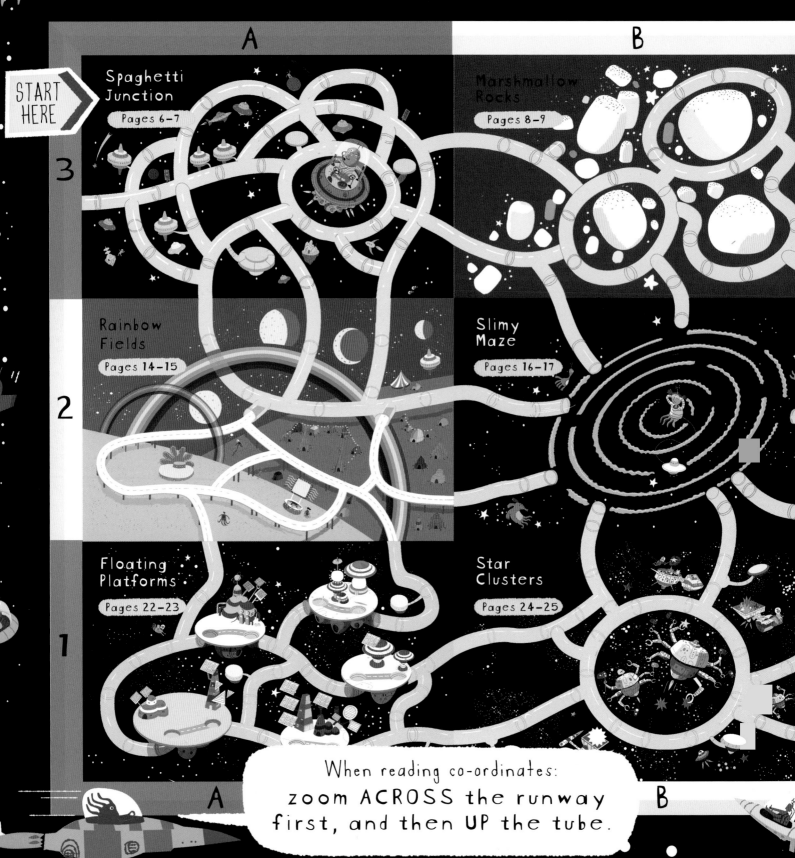

START HERE

When reading co-ordinates:
zoom ACROSS the runway first, and then UP the tube.

What are co-ordinates?

Co-ordinates are a set of letters and numbers that show where something is on a map. The letter comes first, followed by the number, so the rocket is in **(D, 1)**. Look for the co-ordinate symbol throughout the book.

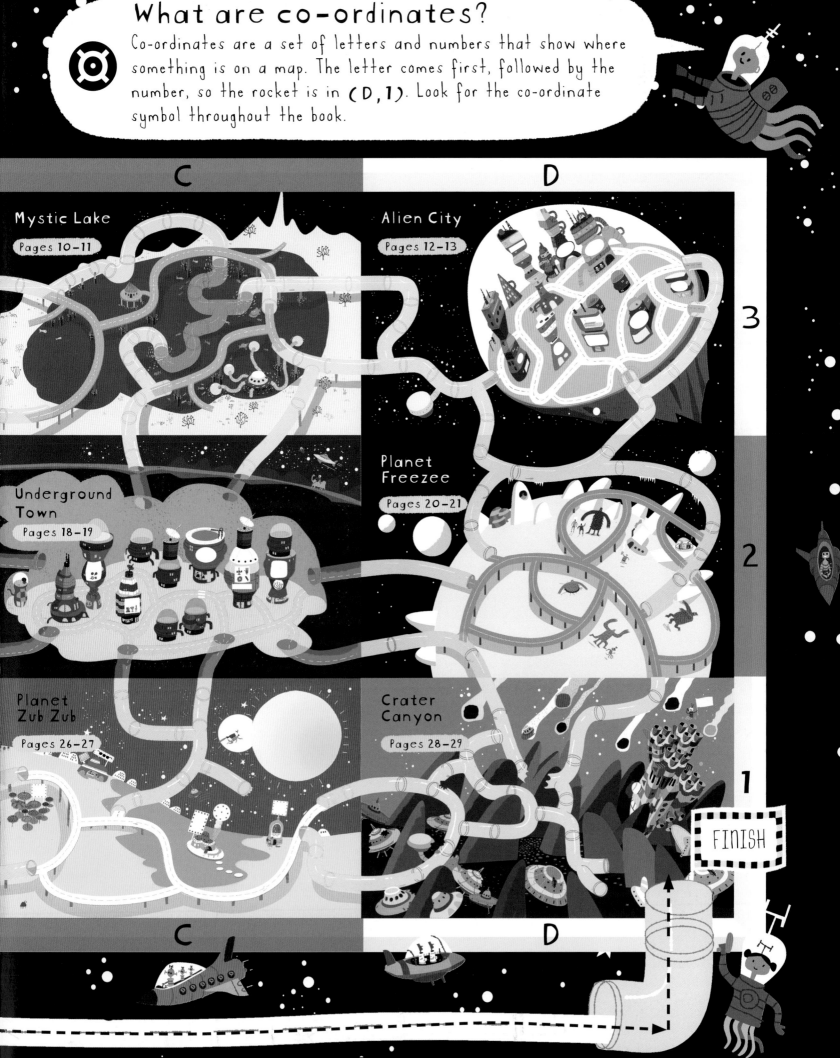

C

D

Mystic Lake
Pages 10-11

Alien City
Pages 12-13

3

Underground Town
Pages 18-19

Planet Freezee
Pages 20-21

2

Planet Zub Zub
Pages 26-27

Crater Canyon
Pages 28-29

1

FINISH

C

D

Yikes! It's very dark down here. The Zeebles have built this amazing place because it gets too hot above ground in the summer. Take a look around, what can you spot?

ZOBOGLOB BATTERY

GLOOPY GLUE

SPACE SPANNER

Go to page 10
MYSTIC LAKE

The swimming pool is almost full. It can only take 10 Zeebles at a time. How many more will fit?

How many orange vehicles can you count?

Go to page 17
SLIMY MAZE

UNDERGROUND TOWN

ROBOT PARTS

ASTRO HELMETS

Haircuts

Go to page 17
SLIMY MAZE

Go to page 26
PLANET ZUB ZUB

Hooray! You're at Crater Canyon. Can you spot where the Zeeble rocket has crashed? Collect your last object and head over to help the Zeebles as they really need you!

ZOBOGLOB BATTERY

GLOOPY GLUE

SPACE SPANNER

Point to who you can see hiding in (B,1).

CRATER CANYON

Go to page 20
PLANET FREEZEE

Go to page 27
PLANET ZUB ZUB

Go to page 27
PLANET ZUB ZUB

STOP

MORE FUN IN SPACE!

Understanding Co-ordinates

Encourage your child to look at other places where they might find co-ordinates, such as in an A-Z map book. Draw a map of space together and plot where you might put the stars and planets.

Counting

Go back through the book and look for more opportunities to encourage counting in space. For example, how many UFOs can you spot? How many asteroids can you see?

Telling the Time

Make a simple clock with your child to encourage them to look closely at telling the time. Use a paper plate, and attach arms using a split pin or pipe cleaners. Fill in the clock face using coloured pens. To go a step further, make paper 'flaps' which can be lifted up to reveal the minutes. Decorate to look like the Moon and stars, or the window of a spaceship.

Recognising Shapes

Make your own rocket! Cut out lots of different 2D shapes from coloured paper. You could use triangles for the nose and wings and a long rectangle for the body. You could even try using 3D shapes with cardboard boxes or plasticine.

Maths Problems and Vocabulary

Go back through the book and look for opportunities to build on mathematic vocabulary and problem solving skills. For example, if there are three Zeebles holding two ice creams each, how many ice creams are there altogether? Are there more pink stars than orange stars?

Length and Height

Using plasticine, make alien creatures with your child. How tall will they be? Perhaps they might have really long arms, and short legs. Line up your aliens in height order, with the shortest first.

Quarto is the authority on a wide range of topics.

Quarto educates, entertains and enriches the lives of our readers—enthusiasts and lovers of hands-on living.

www.quartoknows.com

Written and edited by: Joanna McInerney and the QED team
Designer: Mike Henson
Consultant: Alistair Bryce-Clegg

2016 © Quarto Publishing plc

This edition first published in paperback in 2018 by QED Publishing, an imprint of The Quarto Group.

The Old Brewery, 6 Blundell Street,
London N7 9BH, United Kingdom.
T (0)20 7700 6700 F (0)20 7700 8066
www.QuartoKnows.com

A catalogue record for this book is available from the British Library.

ISBN 978 1 78603 288 1

Manufactured in Guangdong, China TT042018

9 8 7 6 5 4 3 2 1